# Nice Shot, Snoopy

Selected cartoons from
THE WAY OF THE FUSSBUDGET
IS NOT EASY, Vol. III

---

**Charles M. Schulz**

CORONET BOOKS
Hodder and Stoughton

PEANUTS comic strips by
Charles M. Schulz

First published in the United States of
America 1988 by Ballantine Books

Coronet edition 1988

This book comprises a portion of THE
WAY OF THE FUSSBUDGET IS NOT
EASY and is reprinted by arrangement
with Henry Holt and Company, Inc.

**British Library C.I.P.**

Schulz, Charles M.
    (Charles Monroe), *1922–*
    Nice shot, Snoopy:
    selected cartoons from The way of
    the fussbudget is not easy, Vol. 3
    1. American humorous cartoons –
    collections from individual artists
    1. Title
    741.5'973

    ISBN 0 340 48484 5

Printed and bound in Great Britain
for Hodder and Stoughton
Paperbacks, a division of Hodder and
Stoughton Ltd., Mill Road,
Dunton Green, Sevenoaks, Kent
TN13 2YA.
(Editorial Office: 47 Bedford Square,
London WC1B 3DP) by
Cox & Wyman Ltd., Reading.

# Nice Shot, SNOOPY!

I USED TO WONDER WHY I HATED THE KICKOFF..NOW I KNOW
boot! boot!
boot!
boot!
boot!
MY ARMS GET TIRED!
SCHULZ

And for lunch they all had Shrim plooey.
I THINK YOU MEAN SHRIMP LOUIE...
WELL, HOW CAN I BE EXPECTED TO KNOW THAT?
I'VE NEVER EVEN BEEN TO MEXICO!
SCHULZ

HI, SWEETIE! HI! HI!
Dear Snoopy, After I wave to the girl in the red pickup every day, I usually don't have anything else to do.
So lately I have been knitting some stocking caps for me and my friends.
SCHULZ

What I did on my Christmas Vacation. I went outside and looked at the clouds.
They formed beautiful patterns with beautiful colors. I looked at them every morning and every evening.
Which is all I did on my Christmas Vacation.
And what's wrong with that?
SCHULZ

## MORE TITLES AVAILABLE FROM
## HODDER AND STOUGHTON PAPERBACKS

### CHARLES M. SCHULZ

| | | | |
|---|---|---|---|
| ☐ | 37888 3 | Take Charge, Snoopy (75) | £1.95 |
| ☐ | 40855 3 | Good Morning, Snoopy (76) | £1.75 |
| ☐ | 42575 X | You're An Ace, Snoopy (77) | £1.95 |
| ☐ | 42847 3 | How Romantic, Charlie Brown (78) | £1.95 |

*All these books are available at your local bookshop or newsagent, or can be ordered direct from the publisher. Just tick the titles you want and fill in the form below.*

Prices and availability subject to change without notice.

---

Hodder & Stoughton Paperbacks, P.O. Box 11, Falmouth, Cornwall.

Please send cheque or postal order, and allow the following for postage and packing:

U.K. – 55p for one book, plus 22p for the second book, and 14p for each additional book ordered up to a £1.75 maximum.

B.F.P.O. and EIRE – 55p for the first book, plus 22p for the second book, and 14p per copy for the next 7 books, 8p per book thereafter.

OTHER OVERSEAS CUSTOMERS – £1.00 for the first book, plus 25p per copy for each additional book.

Name ................................................................................................

Address ............................................................................................

............................................................................................................